SA/MEN

A CHORAL MEDLEY

H★MI_ _ _N

AN _ _ _JEL MIRANDA

ARRANGED BY LISA DeSPAIN

FABER ♩♩ MUSIC

Hamilton: A Choral Medley is arranged for SA/Men and piano.

Duration: 9 minutes

My Shot is also available for SA/Men (ISBN: 0-571-54007-4)
and SSA (ISBN: 0-571-54008-2)

© 2017 by Faber Music Ltd
First published in 2017 by Faber Music Ltd
Bloomsbury House
74–77 Great Russell Street
London WC1B 3DA
Printed in England by Caligraving Ltd
All rights reserved

ISBN10: 0-571-54006-6
EAN13: 978-0-571-54006-8

To buy Faber Music publications or to find out about the full range of titles available
please contact your local music retailer or Faber Music sales enquiries:

Faber Music Ltd, Burnt Mill, Elizabeth Way, Harlow CM20 2HX
Tel: +44 (0) 1279 82 89 82   Fax: +44 (0) 1279 82 89 83
sales@fabermusic.com   fabermusicstore.com

HAMILTON

A CHORAL MEDLEY

Alexander Hamilton • My Shot • The Schuyler Sisters • The Room Where It Happens
• Helpless • Yorktown (The World Turned Upside Down)

for SA/Men and piano

Arranged by
LISA DeSPAIN

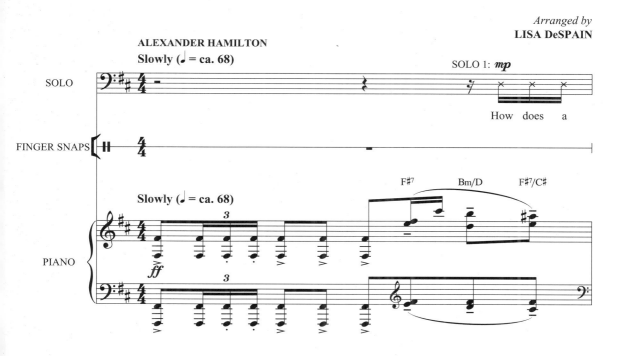

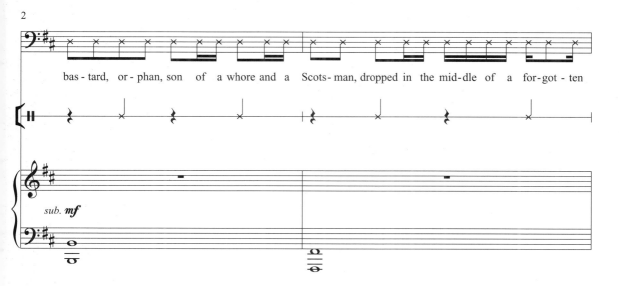

ALEXANDER HAMILTON
Words and Music by LIN-MANUEL MIRANDA
© 2015 5000 BROADWAY MUSIC
All Rights Administered by WB MUSIC CORP
This Arrangement © 2016 5000 BROADWAY MUSIC

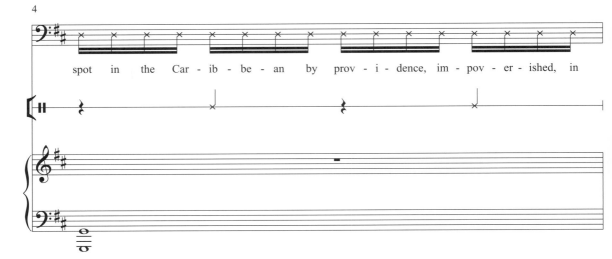

spot in the Car - ib - be - an by prov - i - dence, im - pov - er - ished, in

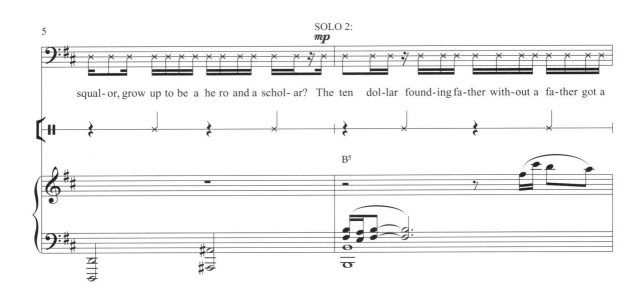

SOLO 2:

squal- or, grow up to be a he ro and a schol- ar? The ten dol-lar found-ing fa-ther with-out a fa-ther got a

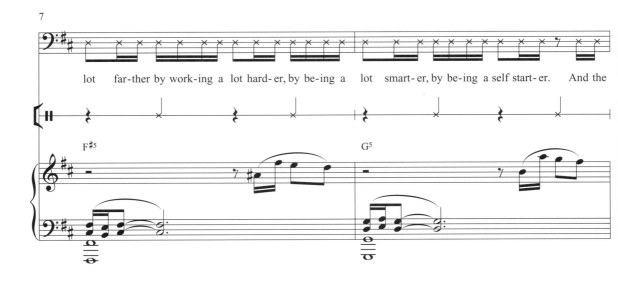

lot far-ther by work-ing a lot hard-er, by be-ing a lot smart- er, by be-ing a self start- er. And the

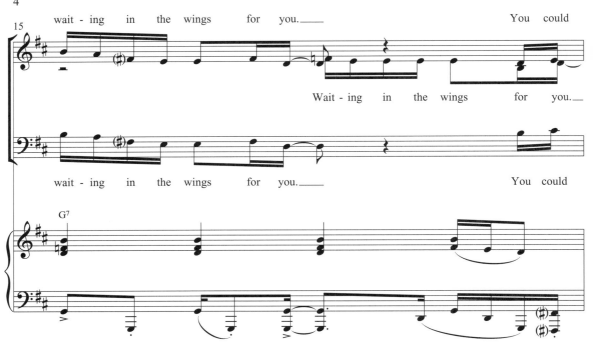

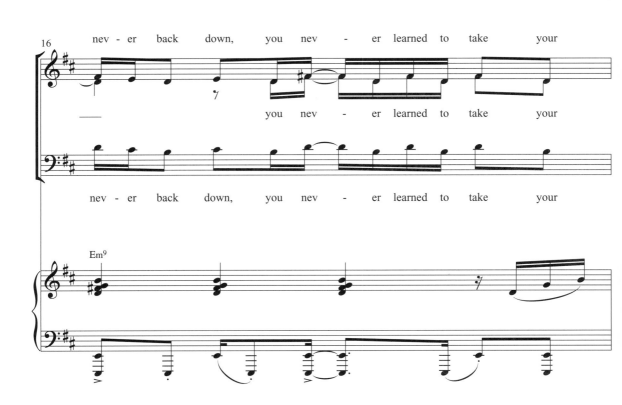

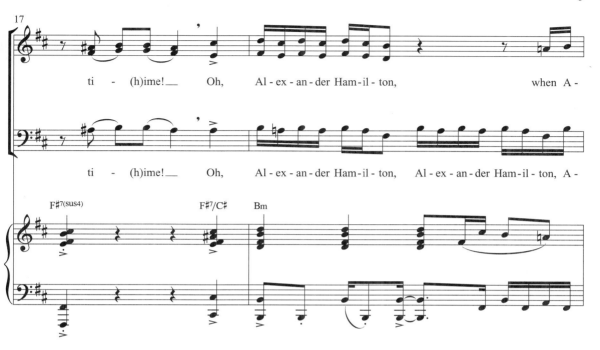

ti - (h)ime!__ Oh, Al - ex - an - der Ham - il - ton, when A -

ti - (h)ime!__ Oh, Al - ex - an - der Ham - il - ton, Al - ex - an - der Ham - il - ton, A -

F#7(sus4)   F#7/C#   Bm

mer - i - ca sings for you,__ will they know what you o - ver-came? Will they know__

mer - i - ca sings for you,__ will they know what you o - ver-came? Will they know__

G7   Em9

25 Faster (♩ = ca. 88)

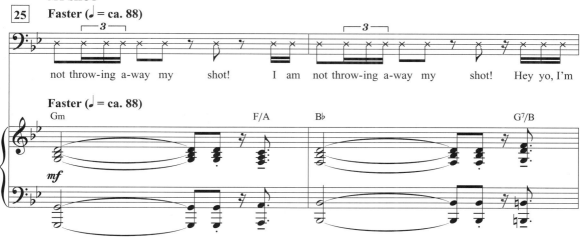

not throw-ing a-way my shot! I am not throw-ing a-way my shot! Hey yo, I'm

27

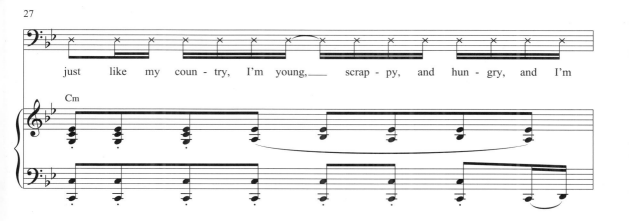

just like my coun-try, I'm young,___ scrap-py, and hun-gry, and I'm

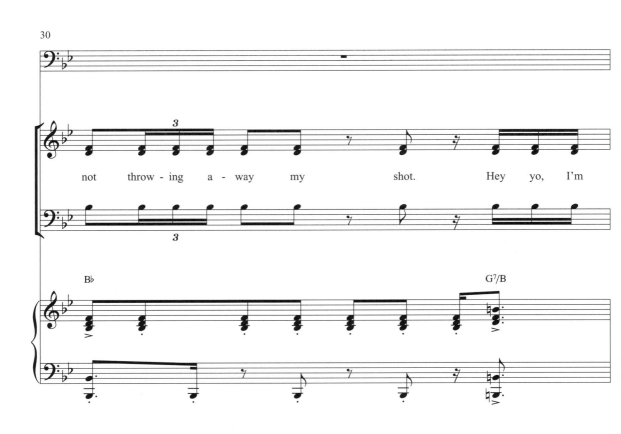

31

just like my coun-try I'm young,___ scrap-py, and hun-gry, and I'm

Cm

Cm/D

32

SOLO 5: *mf*

33

Come on! Let's go! Rise up! When you're liv-ing on your knees,_ you

not throw-ing a-way my shot.

Cm/Eb

D⁷/F♯

Gm

F/A

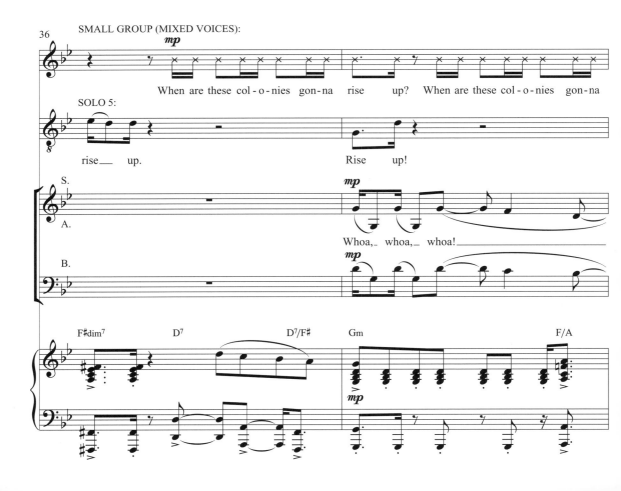

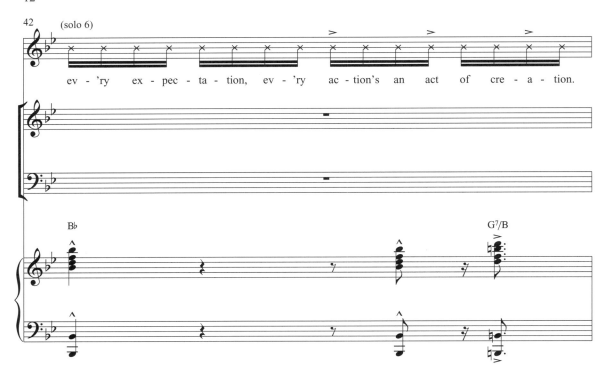

ev - 'ry ex - pec - ta - tion, ev - 'ry ac - tion's an act of cre - a - tion.

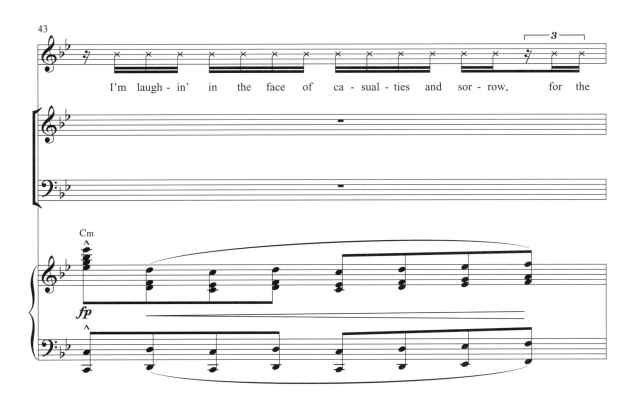

I'm laugh - in' in the face of ca - sual - ties and sor - row, for the

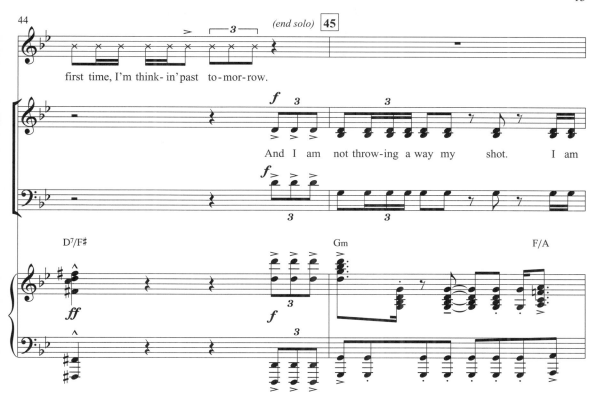

first time, I'm think-in' past to-mor-row.

And I am not throw-ing a way my shot. I am

not throw-ing a - way my shot. Hey yo, I'm

just like my coun - try I'm young,___ scrap - py, and hun - gry, and I'm

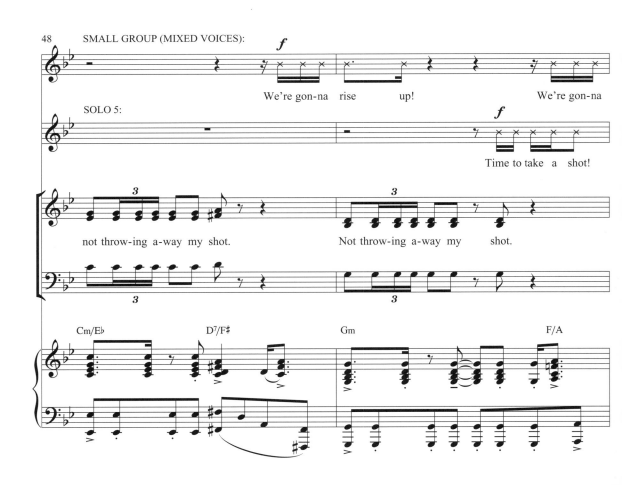

SMALL GROUP (MIXED VOICES):

We're gon-na rise up!   We're gon-na

SOLO 5:

Time to take a shot!

not throw-ing a-way my shot.   Not throw-ing a-way my   shot.

Cm/E♭   D⁷/F♯   Gm   F/A

I've been read-ing *Com-mon Sense* by Thom-as Paine. So men say that I'm in-tense or I'm in-sane.

You want a rev-o-lu-tion? I want a rev-e-la-tion, so lis-ten to my dec-la-ra-tion:

"We

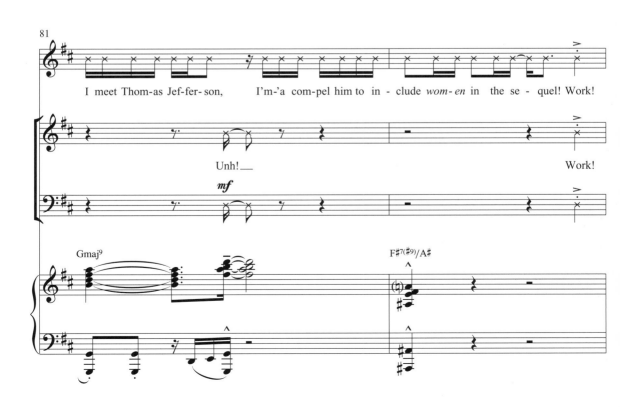

83

'Cause I've been read-ing *Com-mon Sense* by Thom-as Paine.

SOPRANO *only:*

Look a - round,_____ look a - round,_____ the rev -

Bm⁷

f

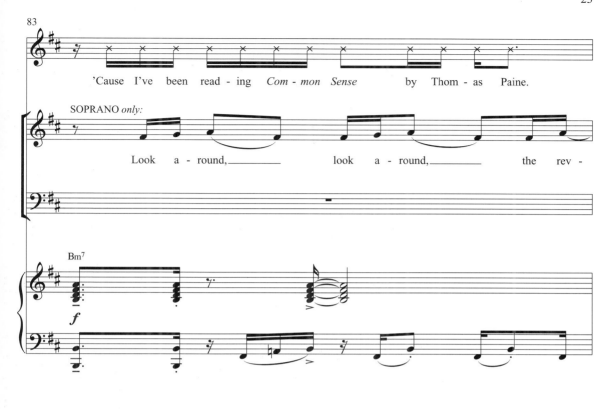

84

So men say that I'm in - tense or I'm in - sane.

- o - lu - tion's hap - pen - ing_____ in New___

D⁶/A

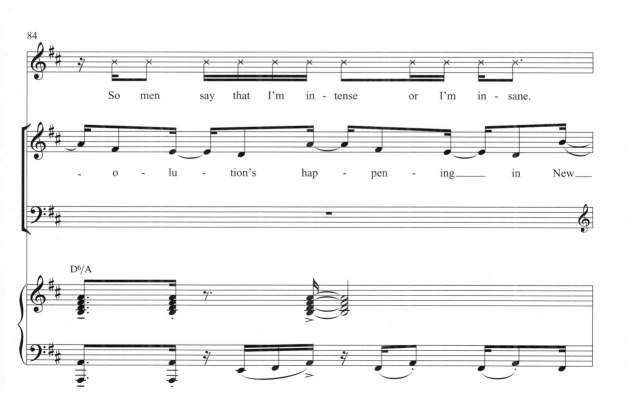

85

You want a rev-o-lu - tion? I want a rev e -la - tion, so lis-ten to my dec - la-ra - tion:

SOPRANO

_____ York.   In New_____ York!   "We

ALTO *mf*

Look a-round,____ look a-round,____ the rev - o-lu - tion's hap - pen - ing.____

Gmaj⁹   F♯m⁷

87

S.

A.

hold these truths to be____ self - ev - i - dent, that all men are cre-at-ed e - qual."_____

Look a-round,____ look a-round____ at how luck-y we are____ to be a-live right____ now.

B. *mf*

Bm⁷   D⁶/A

Look a-round,_ look a-round_ at how luck-y we are_ to be a-live right_ now!

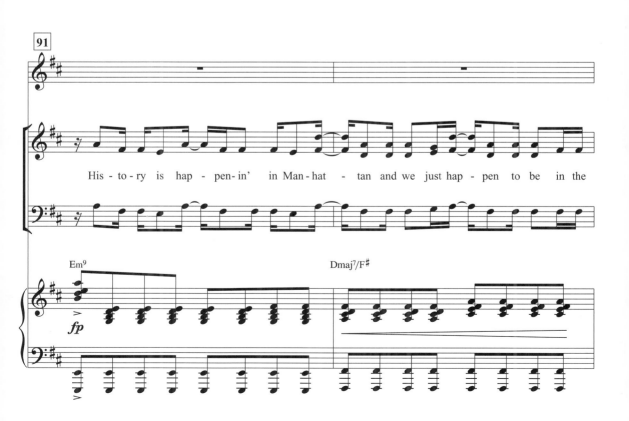

His-to-ry is hap-pen-in' in Man-hat - tan and we just hap-pen to be in the

THE ROOM WHERE IT HAPPENS

THE ROOM WHERE IT HAPPENS
Words and Music by LIN-MANUEL MIRANDA
© 2015 5000 BROADWAY MUSIC
All Rights Administered by WB MUSIC CORP
This Arrangement © 2016 5000 BROADWAY MUSIC
All Rights Reserved.   Used by Permission.

28

32

118 SMALL GROUP (MIXED VOICES):

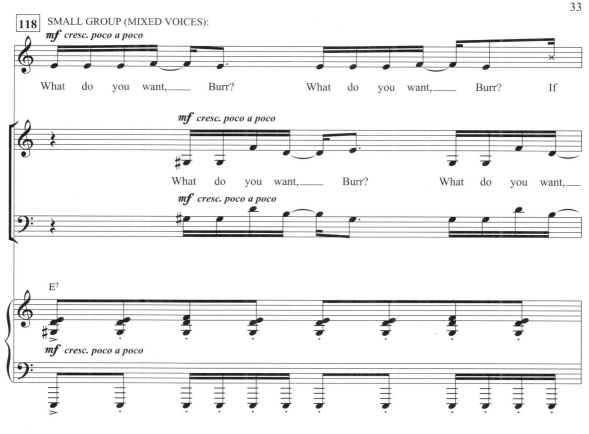

What do you want,___ Burr? What do you want,___ Burr? If

What do you want,___ Burr? What do you want,___

(end small group)

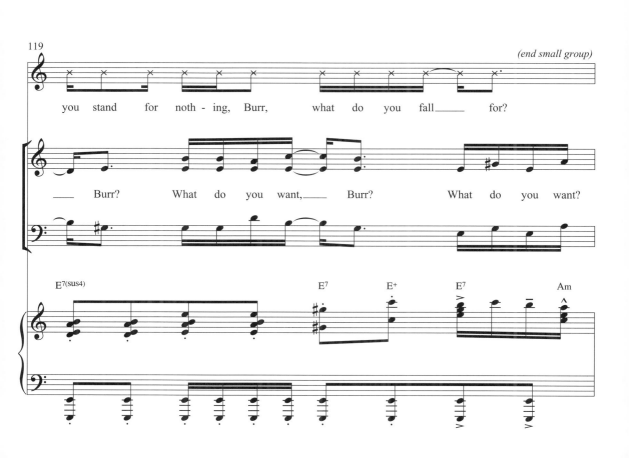

you stand for noth - ing, Burr, what do you fall___ for?

___ Burr? What do you want,___ Burr? What do you want?

help - less!_____ Down for the count, and I'm drown - in' in 'em.

F(add9)   F/A   B♭

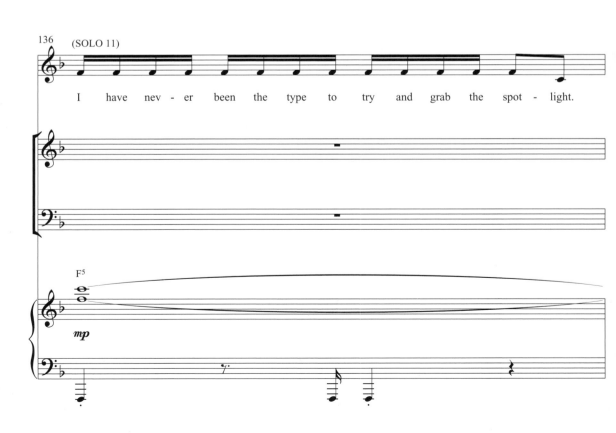

(SOLO 11)

I have nev - er been the type to try and grab the spot - light.

F5

mp

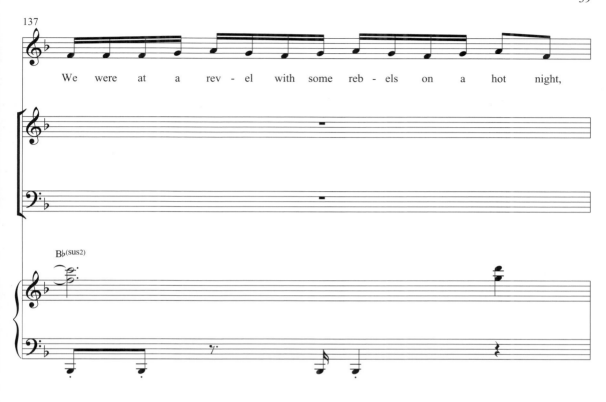

We were at a rev - el with some reb - els on a hot night,

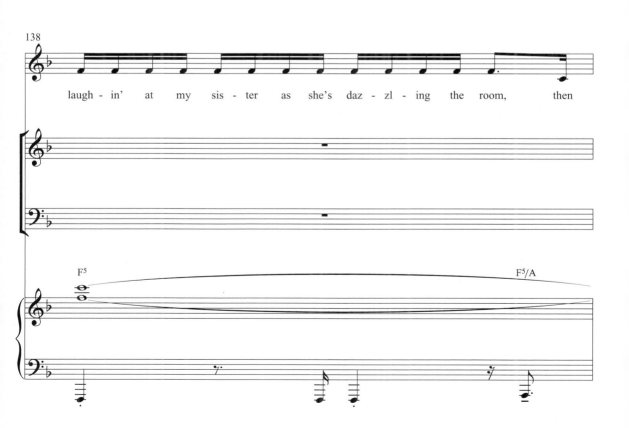

laugh - in' at my sis - ter as she's daz - zl - ing the room, then

you walked in   and my heart went "boom!"   My sis-ter made her way a cross the room to

Oooh._____

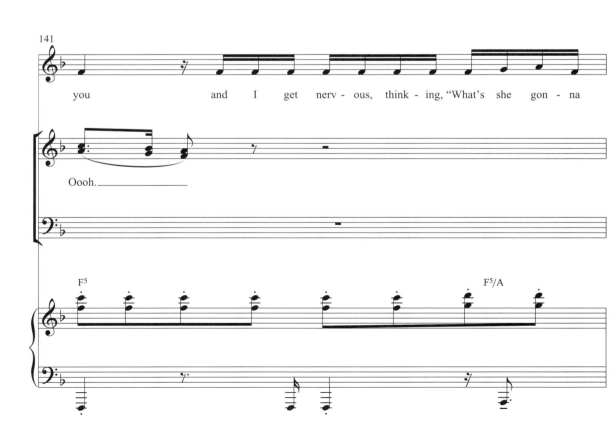

you   and   I   get   nerv-ous, think-ing, "What's she gon - na

Oooh._____

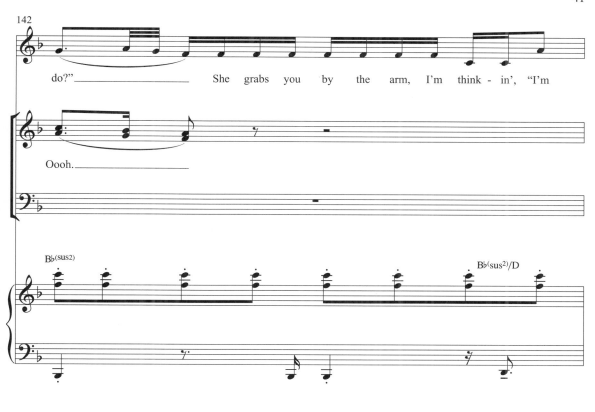

do?" _____ She grabs you by the arm, I'm think-in', "I'm

Oooh._____

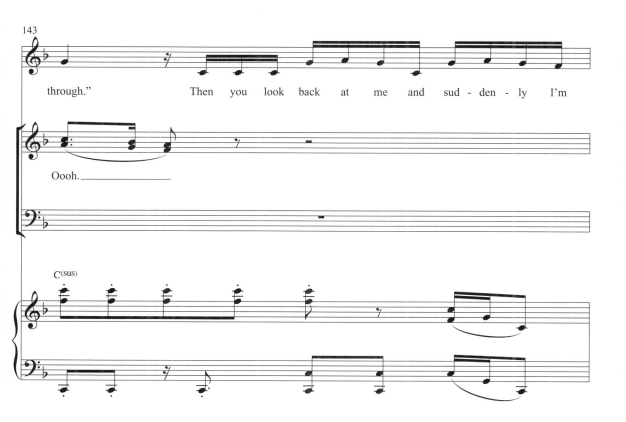

through." Then you look back at me and sud-den-ly I'm

Oooh._____

44

YORKTOWN (THE WORLD TURNED UPSIDE DOWN)

157 SOLO 13: *mf*

I i-mag-ine death so much it feels more like a mem-o - ry. This is where it

Sev-en teen Eight - y - one.

G   Dm   C

159

gets me: on my feet, the en - e - my a-head of me.   If this is the end of me, at least I have a friend with me,

G   Dm   C

161

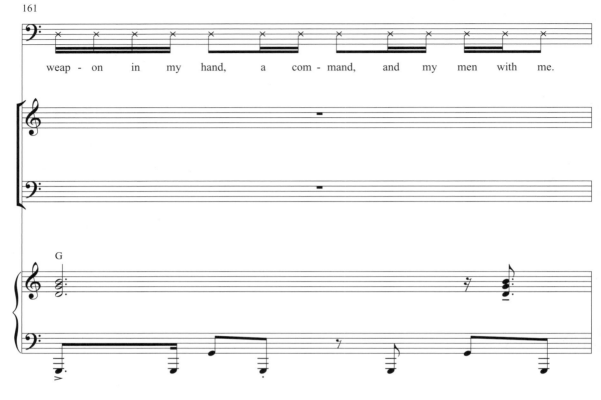

weap - on in my hand, a com - mand, and my men with me.

162

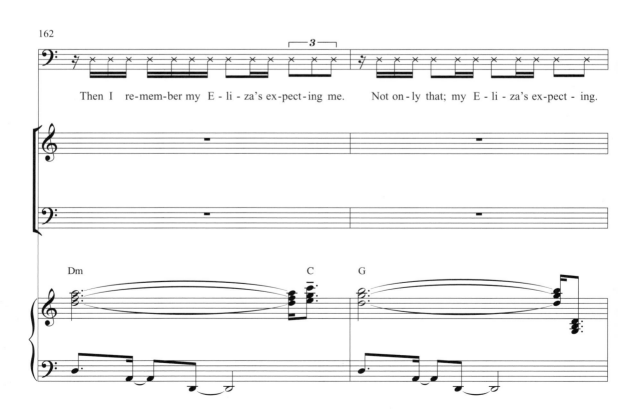

Then I re-mem-ber my E - li - za's ex-pect - ing me. Not on - ly that; my E - li - za's ex-pect - ing.

168

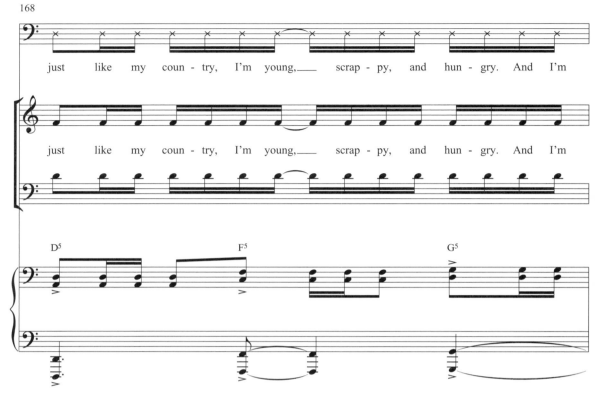

169

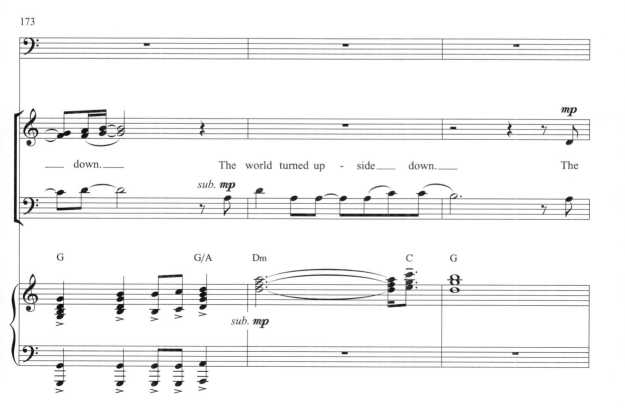

176

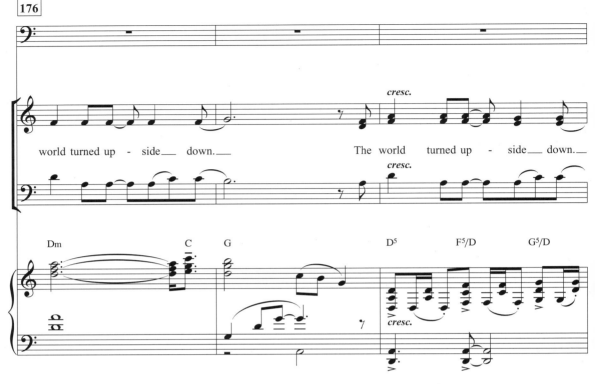

world turned up - side___ down.___ The world turned up - side___ down.

Dm   C   G   D⁵   F⁵/D   G⁵/D

179

___ The world turned up - side___ down,___ down,___ down,___

F/B♭   C⁵/B♭   D⁵/B♭   Dm/A   G⁽ˢᵘˢ⁾/A G/A